INTRODUCTION

The units

Science at Work is a series of 24 science and technology units for students aged 14–19. Each unit consists of a students' book and a teachers' guide. Each provides a course of study of about 15 hours (typically covering half a term in a secondary school). The units are self-contained, and can be taken in any order.

The students' books

The students' books provide information, practical investigations and questions. Students are able to work from the books at their own pace. Generally, the questions become more difficult towards the end of each section.

There is a summary of what the student should have learned at the end of each students' book. The material has been checked to ensure that the reading level is as low as possible, and every experiment has been checked for safety.

INVESTIGATIONS
Most investigations begin with a stated purpose. The required apparatus is then listed, and instructions for the investigation given (in words and pictures). Finally, the students are asked questions which help them record their results and draw conclusions.

INFORMATION
Appropriate information sections from the real world follow most investigations. Questions are also asked about some of these information sections.

The teachers'

Each unit has a teachers' gu information and assistance

This teachers' guide contai...
course and unit objectives
hints on introducing and teaching the unit
apparatus lists (for technicians)
safety procedures
new scientific words (which students may have difficulty reading)
answers to selected questions in the students' book
a resource list
extension work for more able students.

EXTENSION WORK
The *Science at Work* course was written with the needs of less able students in mind. However, no matter how carefully a school or college identifies these students, any class will contain students who learn at different speeds – because of variation in ability, motivation, meticulousness or attendance.

The extension work is intended to help teachers solve these problems; in particular it is designed to extend the conceptual level of the work for those students who have the potential to achieve GCSE grade C.

Pages 11–19 are copyright but copies may be made without fee or prior permission provided that these copies are used solely within the institution for which the book is purchased. For copying in any other circumstances (*e.g.* by an external resource centre) prior written permission must be obtained from the Publishers and a fee may be payable.

Examining the course

Science at Work is derived from a successful and well proven modular scheme developed by teachers in the Manchester LEA. Following the success of CSE courses in many areas of the country, most GCSE Examining Groups now offer suitable syllabuses. You are advised to contact the science subject officer at any of the GCSE Groups for further details.

AIMS OF THE COURSE

1 To provide a flexible modular science and technology course based on non-sequential study units. Though developed predominantly for less able students, the course caters for students capable of a range of GCSE grades by the use of the extension work.
2 To develop students' thinking in scientific methodology and the approach to problem solving.
3 To give knowledge and understanding of science and technology relevant to students' interests, environment, and future work and leisure needs.
4 To develop students' interest in science and their enjoyment of science.
5 To provide a wide range of practical experiences and to develop practical skills.
6 To develop the ability to work both independently and as a member of a team.

GENERAL OBJECTIVES OF THE COURSE

1 To develop the ability to carry out experimental procedures and written work according to instructions.
2 To develop manipulative skills in handling equipment and an awareness of safe practice.
3 To develop powers of accurate observation.
4 To develop the ability to check statements and assertions against tests of observation and experiment.
5 To develop skill in handling and interpretation of data.
6 To develop the ability to look for and make generalisations (this objective is likely to be achieved by only the ablest pupils).
7 To be able to understand and recall the factual content of the material.
8 To develop communications skills – verbal, written, graphical and mathematical.
9 To develop the ability to apply knowledge gained.
10 To encourage pride in neatly and accurately produced work.
11 To develop awareness of the responsible use of science and technology.

OBJECTIVES OF THE ELECTRONICS UNIT

In their work on *Electronics* students will find out:
● that electronic equipment is affecting their lives in many ways
● that a complete circuit is needed for electricity to flow from one place to another
● that the brightness of a lamp indicates how much electricity is flowing through it
● that the higher the resistance in the circuit, the less electricity flows
● that a variable resistor can be used to alter the amount of electricity flowing
● that variable resistors are used to control the volume and brightness of audio equipment and TVs
● that a diode only conducts electricity in one direction
● that a thermistor operates like a heat dependent resistor, usually giving a high resistance at a low temperature
● that an LDR is a light dependent resistor, giving a low resistance when light shines on it
● that LDRs and thermistors do not have on–off conditions
● that an LED acts like a diode, but emits light when it is conducting
● that LEDs, LDRs, diodes and thermistors have many applications in electronic circuits
● that reed and relay switches operate when they are placed in magnetic fields
● that a relay switch uses a small amount of electricity in one circuit to switch on a larger amount in a different circuit
● that a transistor can be used as a switch or to amplify small amounts of electricity
● that a small amount of electricity in the base circuit switches on a larger amount in the collector circuit
● that LDRs and thermistors can be used with transistors in circuits to operate output devices using changes in light and temperature conditions
● that one stage and two stage amplifiers can be made using transistors
● that a simple radio receiver circuit produces a louder sound if it is used with an amplifier
● that soldered components are used in 'real' electronic circuits
● that the techniques and components studied in this book enable the student to design and use a wide range of electronic circuits.

TEACHING THE ELECTRONICS UNIT

Teaching the unit

The students' book contains fifteen chapters. Most chapters have activity and information pages. Chapter 15 consists of two design problems. There are sequential questions within each section. Each question should be answered in the student's notebook.

In the pages that follow, each section is discussed with reference to apparatus needed per working group; new technological and scientific words; safety and teaching hints; answers to questions (where appropriate); resources.

Equipment

Students may work using either soldered circuits or Locktronics equipment. The components needed for this unit are available from Lock International plc, PO Box OL82, Neville Street, Oldham OL9 6LF, Lancashire. They can be bought separately, or as a kit. The Locktronics kit is designed for six students arranged in three pairs. Each pair can study chapters 1, 2 and 3 simultaneously. Then the pairs should be rotated so that one pair studies chapter 4, the second pair studies chapters 5 and 6, and the third pair studies chapter 7. Students can then go on to study later chapters. A list of components that are needed to do all the investigations is given here:

18 connector links
3 press switch carriers
5 lampholder carriers
3 resistor carriers 100 Ω
3 resistor carriers 180 Ω
3 resistor carriers 270 Ω
3 resistor carriers 1 kΩ
1 resistor carrier 2.2 kΩ
1 resistor carrier 5.6 kΩ
2 resistor carriers 10 kΩ
2 resistor carriers 270 kΩ
3 variable resistor carriers 250 Ω
1 variable resistor carrier 10 kΩ
1 variable resistor carrier 100 kΩ
1 variable capacitor carrier 0–200 pF
1 diode carrier (1N4001)
1 diode carrier (0A91)
2 transistor carriers r.h. facing
1 oscillator coil carrier
1 crossover link carrier
2 S.P. C/O switch carriers
2 capacitor carriers 10 µF
1 ferrite rod
6 lamps 6 V 40 mA M.E.S. or 6 V 60 mA

1 thermistor carrier (KR 681 CW)
1 thermistor carrier (KR 472 CW)
1 relay carrier 6 volt
1 reed switch carrier
1 reed switch and coil carrier
1 LED
1 buzzer
1 LDR

The following items are offered separately:

2 earphone/microphones
3 LK750 baseboards
1 small motor carrier

The following items are not sold by Locktronics:

soldering iron
solder
copper wire
eye protection

 This work is safe because it uses low voltages, but students should **never** experiment with mains voltages.

3

DETAILED TEACHING NOTES

The following items should be assembled as a basic student's kit: circuit board, 6 connector links; 1 press switch; 2 battery connectors; 2 lampholders with 6 V, 0.04 A lamps; 9 V battery. The apparatus lists for each chapter will include the additional components required for each experiment. The quantities are those needed by each working group.

> ⚠ The teacher should check any circuit that contains a transistor *before* the students connect the battery.

1 ELECTRONICS

ELECTRONIC DEVICES
(students' book page 1)

Q1 Any electronic equipment will do for the list. The teacher could read this with the students and discuss the effect of electronics on them.

2 LAMPS AND RESISTORS

(students' book pages 2 and 3)

Apparatus: basic kit; resistors 100 Ω, 180 Ω and 270 Ω
New words: circuit, voltage, resistor

In the first exercise it will be necessary to check that students understand the use of the circuit board and are able to translate symbols into circuits. It is not possible to damage any components electrically so students may be allowed complete freedom provided that they **do not short-circuit the battery**. It will be necessary to discuss voltage, brightness of the lamp and the amount of electricity flowing (current). An informal explanation of resistance will be necessary.

Q1 9 V.
Q2 6 V.
Q3 Because a lot of electricity is flowing through the lamp.
Q4 It connects the battery.
Q5 The lamp goes dim.
Q6 The resistor is reducing the amount of electricity going through the lamp.
Q7 Yes.
Q8 Dimmer or out.
Q9 Brighter.
Q10 No.

3 VARIABLE RESISTORS

(students' book page 4)

Apparatus: basic kit; variable resistor 250 Ω; small electric motor
New words: variable resistor, resistance

Q1 Any circuit which will work will do. An example is shown below.

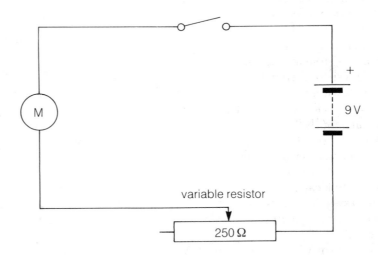

VARIABLE RESISTORS
(students' book page 5)

Extension sheet '1 Lamps and resistors' may be used here.

Q1 Less, dimmer. More, brighter.

4 DIODES, THERMISTORS AND LDRS

A LAMP CIRCUIT WITH A DIODE
(students' book page 6)

Apparatus: basic kit; diode 1N4001
New words: diode, thermistor, light dependent resistor (LDR)

The diode is substituted for the resistors in chapter 1. No damage is possible. Allow free use of the kit.

Q1 B.
Q2 B.
Q3 It stops the electricity flowing through the lamp completely, but only in one direction.

A LAMP CIRCUIT WITH A THERMISTOR
(students' book page 7)

Apparatus: basic kit; thermistor KR 681 CW; glass beaker; 2 connecting wires

A thermistor is substituted for the diode. No damage is possible. Provide a beaker of very hot water when it is needed.

Extension sheet '2 Thermistors' may be used here.

Q1 Lamp should not light.   **Q5** Let it cool.
Q2 Lamp should not light.   **Q6** No.
Q3 Lamp should light.   **Q7** Low, high.
Q4 Heat it up.

A LAMP CIRCUIT WITH A LIGHT DEPENDENT RESISTOR
(students' book page 8)

Apparatus: basic kit; LDR; torch

An LDR is substituted for the thermistor. No damage is possible.

Q1 Lamp should not light.
Q2 Yes.
Q3 Lamp should light.
Q4 Low, high.
Q5

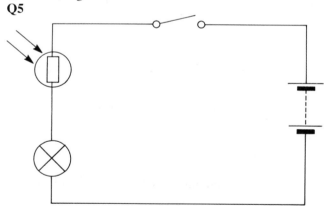

A CIRCUIT WITH A MYSTERY
(students' book page 9)

Apparatus: basic kit; light emitting diode component
New word: components

This exercise allows open-ended investigation, but a simple circuit is needed. (See the circuit on page 6 of the students' book.)

Q1 Most like a diode. It conducts in one direction.

DIODES AND LIGHT DEPENDENT RESISTORS
(students' book page 10)

It would be useful to read these two information pages with the students to explain difficult words to them.

LIGHT EMITTING DIODES AND THERMISTORS
(students' book page 11)

New words: light emitting diode (LED), indicator lamp, filament lamp, thermometer, thermostat

5 REED SWITCHES

(students' book pages 12 and 13)

Apparatus: basic kit; extra 9 V battery;
4 battery connectors; reed switch; reed switch in coil; small magnet (2.5–7.5 cm long); 30 cm length of thread
New words: reed switch, reed coil, normally closed, normally open

A FRIEND'S PROBLEM
(students' book page 14)

Q1   a)   b)   c)

Q2 a) LED.   b) Thermistor.
  c) LDR.   d) Diode.

Reeds and relays should be understood as variations on the mechanically operated switch. The reed is a magnetically operated switch. The relay is an electro-magnetically operated switch (see page 14 of this teachers' guide).

Q1 The magnet.
Q2 Depends on student's skill – probably too fast to count.
Q3 Lamp X should not light.
Q4 Because you can hear the reed switch work.
Q5 Lamp Y should light.
Q6 Because the coil acts as a resistor and reduces the electricity flowing through the lamp.

This problem is open-ended. Any equipment the students ask for should be provided, but the design should be checked before they proceed with making or testing anything.

Example circuit:

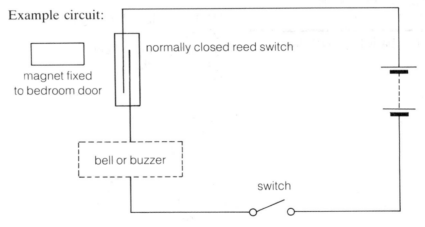

When the door is opened the reed switch contact will close and complete the circuit, so setting off the bell (as long as the switch is closed).

6 RELAY SWITCHES

(students' book page 15)

Apparatus: basic kit; extra 9 V battery; relay switch; small electric motor

Extension sheet '3 Relays' may be used here.

Q1 They both work.
Q2 The relay clicks.
Q3 It shows that the relay works.

Q4

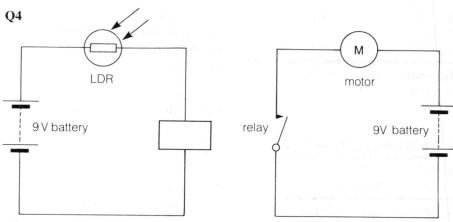

7 TRANSISTORS

USING TRANSISTORS
(students' book page 16)

Apparatus: basic kit; resistor 10 kΩ;
transistor
New words: transistor, amplify

 Transistors are damaged if they or the battery are connected the wrong way round in the circuit, resulting in the current flowing backwards in the collector circuit. Damage can also be caused by overloading the base or the collector circuit. Never allow a base resistance lower than 1 kΩ when 9 V batteries are used. Spare transistors should be on hand.

By discussion, try to establish an understanding that:
a) small changes in the base current cause larger changes in the collector current and
b) large changes in the base current cause the transistor to 'switch' the collector current 'on' or 'off'.

Q1 Lamp X should not light. Lamp Y should light.
Q2 Lamps should not light.

BASE AND COLLECTOR CIRCUITS
(students' book page 17)

New words: base, collector, emitter

Q1 Does, is, is.
Q2 The electricity stops flowing.

CHANGING THE CURRENT IN THE BASE CIRCUIT
(students' book page 18)

Apparatus: basic kit; transistor;
resistor 5.6 kΩ; variable resistor
100 kΩ

Extension sheet '4 Transistors' may be used here.

Teaching notes as for the previous experiment apply.

Q1 You can vary the electricity flowing through the transistor.
Q2 Lamp goes bright or dim.
Q3 Slow changes.
Q4 Amplifies a current. Makes a small current change in one part of the circuit into a larger change in another part.

8 LIGHT OPERATED SWITCHES

AN AUTOMATIC PARKING LIGHT
(students' book page 19)

Apparatus: basic kit; 2 resistors 1 kΩ;
variable resistor 10 kΩ; 2 transistors;
LDR; resistor 10 kΩ

Transistors will be damaged if they or the battery are connected the wrong way round in the circuit.

The LDR is effectively a light controlled variable resistor in the base circuit. Step C, balancing the circuit against ambient light conditions, is not easy and students may need help. The current from the LDR is amplified by the first transistor and switches on the second transistor.

Q1 The lamp lights.
Q2 Transistor and/or LDR.
Q3 A burglar alarm (that goes on in torch light) or a burglar alarm for a drawer *etc.*

OTHER USES FOR A LIGHT
OPERATED SWITCH
(students' book page 20)

Apparatus: circuit from the previous experiment; diode 1N4001; small motor; relay; torch

9 FROST AND STEAM ALARMS

A FROST ALARM
(students' book page 21)

Apparatus: basic kit; 2 transistors; thermistor KR472CW; 2 resistors 1 kΩ; variable resistor 10 kΩ; resistor 10 kΩ; resistor 5.6 kΩ; beaker of fresh ice

A STEAM ALARM
(students' book page 22)

Apparatus: basic kit; 2 transistors; thermistor KR472CW; resistor 10 kΩ; 2 resistors 1 kΩ; variable resistor 10 kΩ; resistor 5.6 kΩ; tripod; Bunsen burner; gauze; heatproof mat; leads with crocodile clips; conical flask; eye protection

10 A RAIN ALARM

(students' book pages 23 and 24)

Apparatus: basis kit; 2 transistors; 3 resistors 1 kΩ; variable resistor 100 kΩ; 2 wire probes; 2 beakers; buzzer; diode 1N4001; relay; clamp stand; 2 wire probes; 2 beakers

The motor current is too high for the collector of the second transistor so a relay and protecting diode are used. The diode short circuits the back EMF (electromotive force) produced by the relay coil and prevents a reverse current passing through the transistor.

Q1 LDR.
Q2 White line follower *etc.*

 Transistors will be damaged if they or the battery are connected the wrong way round in the circuit.

Discuss the use of the heat controlled variable resistor (thermistor) in the base circuit and the similarity with chapter 8.

Q1 Thermistor.
Q2 Using a variable resistor and a thermometer so the lamp just lights when the thermistor is in water at 10 °C.
Q3 Automatic electric kettle, device to tell when an oven is at required temperature, *etc.*
Q4 Same circuit as for step A on page 20 of the students' book, but with a thermistor instead of the LDR and a bell instead of the motor.

 Transistors will be damaged if they or the battery are connected the wrong way round in the circuit.

 Students must wear eye protection.

Students will need to work in pairs.

Placing the thermistor in the position shown in this circuit reverses the effect it had in the previous experiment – that is, the high temperature and low resistance drain the base current. It switches transistor 1 off (there is no collector current) and the base current of transistor 2 is now able to flow, which switches on collector current through transistor 2.

Extension sheet '5 Electronic devices' may be used here.

Q1 Thermistor and variable resistor positions are swopped.
Q2 Fire alarm or chip pan alarm to warn if something is getting too hot, or a tropical fish tank alarm to warn if the water is becoming too cold.

 Transistors will be damaged if they or the battery are connected the wrong way round in the circuit.

The wire probes can be made from two lengths of bare 18 swg copper mounted in a cork and soldered to flex leads with 4 mm plugs.

The probes act in a similar way to the thermistor in the steam alarm. The relay or diode is required to handle large currents.

Extension sheet '6 A water detector' may be used here.

Q1 The lamp goes out.
Q2 Variable resistor or probe. It is important to stress that the sensitivity here is different to that which an LDR has to light, for example.
Q3 The lamp.
Q4 Any reasonable drawing.
Q5 Probes or transistor.

Q6 Transistor.

Q7 To handle a large amount of electricity which would overheat the transistor, but which is needed to work the buzzer.

Any simple and adequate explanation of water sensor in use will do for the extension questions.

MOISTURE SENSITIVE CIRCUITS
(students' book page 24)

New words: moisture detector

11 AMPLIFIERS

(students' book page 25)

Apparatus: basic kit; 2 capacitors 10 μF; 2 microphones; 2 transistors; 2 resistors 270 kΩ; resistor 10 kΩ
New words: amplifier, capacitor, microphone

 The transistor will be damaged if it or the battery is connected the wrong way round in the circuit.

Students will need to work in pairs.

In this circuit, the transistor is amplifying rather than 'switching'. Small changes in the current of the base circuit are caused by variations induced in the microphone.

The two stage amplifier is based on the same principle as the single stage amplifier in the previous chapter. The capacitors must be connected with correct polarity.

Extension sheet '7 Light emitting diodes and phototransistors' may be used here.

Q1 Two stage.

Q2 The two transistors.

12 A TELEPHONE CIRCUIT

(students' book page 26)

Apparatus: basic kit; crossover; 2 transistors; 2 resistors 270 kΩ; resistor 2.2 kΩ; 2 capacitors 10 μF; 2 microphones; 2 two-way switches

 The transistors will be damaged if they or the battery are connected the wrong way round in the circuit.

Students will need to work in pairs.

This is the same two stage amplifier as the students built in the previous chapter. The circuit is complicated by some difficult switching circuitry in order to achieve the two-way function. Check students' work before using the battery. Short 4 mm plug leads may be used instead of crossovers.

Microphone 2 could be changed for a 15 Ω loudspeaker and the circuit used as a loudspeaker.

Q1 Two.

Q2 Transistors.

Q3 A telephone circuit, a P.A. circuit, a radio, a baby 'listener' *etc.*

13 A RADIO RECEIVER

(students' book page 27)

Apparatus: basic kit; transistor; diode 0A81; 2 resistors 10 kΩ; variable capacitor 200 pF; capacitor 10 μF; aerial coil and ferrite rod; microphone; 30 m of 26 g copper wire; connection to earth; selection of resistors

 The transistor will be damaged if it is connected the wrong way round in the circuit.

Tuned circuits are probably too difficult a concept for low ability students. Allow satisfaction from function rather than complete understanding. For good reception, the aerial should be at least 30 m of 26 g bare or covered copper wire with a 4 mm plug fitted. Laboratory plumbing is sometimes isolated from the earth by inserting a section of plastic pipe in the main. If this is the case, run a length of wire from a piece of copper rod buried in firm soil to a convenient 'earth point' in the laboratory. **Do not earth to a mains socket.**

In step E the signal strength may be improved by altering the resistance of the base circuit of the amplifier. Allow students to experiment with fixed or variable resistors to a maximum value of approximately $500\,k\Omega$. Do not allow a resistance smaller than $10\,k\Omega$ in the base circuit. In some areas a two stage amplifier may be required.

Extension sheet '8 Integrated circuits' may be used here.

Q1 Not loud enough.

Q2 An amplifying circuit.

Q3 Make sound louder.

Q4 An extra amplifier.

 There is some risk of burns from the soldering iron. Use a low voltage iron if at all possible. Make sure that students' hands are clean and dry. There is a greater hazard from allowing the hot iron to come into contact with the mains lead. Warn students and provide a suitable stand or resting pad for the iron. The cable should have a heat-resistant sleeve. Students should wash their hands after using solder. Students must also wear eye protection.

14 SOLDERED CIRCUITS

SOLDERING
(students' book pages 28 and 29)

Apparatus: scrap wood; 18 mm brass panel pins; hammer; ruler; emery cloth; cloth; 26 g bare copper wire; soldering iron; wire cutters; resin-cored solder; tweezers; heatproof mat; eye protection

New words: soldering, bit

SOLDERING
(students' book page 29)

New words: alloy, resin

A SOLDERED (PERMANENT) RADIO
(students' book page 30)

Apparatus: piece of wood, hammer; 18 mm brass panel pins; ruler; pencil; emery cloth; cloth; 26 g copper wire; soldering iron; heatproof mat; wire cutters; resin-cored solder; tweezers; battery 9 V; 2 battery connectors; resistor $10\,k\Omega$; resistor $270\,k\Omega$; transistor; variable capacitor 200 pF; diode 0A91; aerial coil and ferrite rod; connection to earth; capacitor $10\,\mu F$; microphone; aerial (30 m of 26 g copper wire); circuit diagram; eye protection

Q1 Safer and easier to use.

Q2 Tin and lead.

Q3 To make a perfect joint.

 The transistor will be damaged if it or the battery is connected the wrong way round in the circuit.

 Students must wear eye protection.

Any circuit from chapters 5–12 can be prepared to dimensions and spacings similar to those given for the radio circuit.

Students should nail or paste the circuit diagram, shown on page 11 of this guide, to the wood base and use brass or steel pins as component posts.

Capacitors, diodes and transistors must be protected from heat by gripping the wire with pliers or tweezers, as shown on page 29 and in step B on page 30 of the students' book. Components may be purchased from radio suppliers such as RS Components Ltd, PO Box 99, Birchington Road, Corby, Northamptonshire NN17 9RS.

15 DESIGN PROJECTS

(students' book pages 31 and 32)

Apparatus: basic kit; any other apparatus

This exercise provides an open-ended project. Provide circuit and any other reasonable materials that students ask for.

PROJECT 1: SMOKE DETECTOR

This can be the same circuit as on page 19 of the students' book but with a relay and buzzer. The buzzer does not sound provided that the lamp shines on the LDR. If the smoke is too thick it is as if the LDR has been covered and the transistor switches.

PROJECT 2: COMPUTER PROTECTION

The thermistor is calibrated to switch the motor on at 25 °C. (A relay can switch on the motor.) This is similar to the circuit on page 22 of the students' book.

Extension: Add a lamp to the circuit.

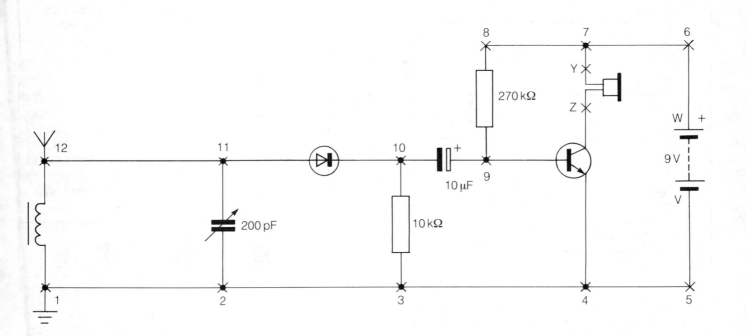

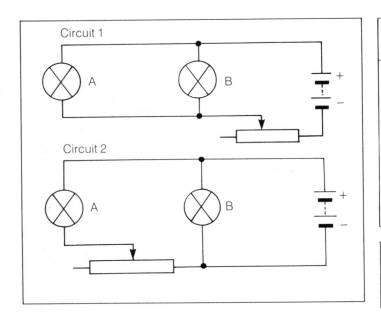

	first figure	second figure	number of noughts	
Black	0	0	0	
Brown	1	1	1	0
Red	2	2	2	00
Orange	3	3	3	000
Yellow	4	4	4	0 000
Green	5	5	5	00 000
Blue	6	6	6	000 000
Purple	7	7	7	0 000 000
Grey	8	8	8	00 000 000
White	9	9	9	000 000 000

1	2	3	4
brown	red	yellow	silver

Q1 Connect up circuit 1, shown above, and vary the resistance. What happens to the brightness of the lamps A and B?

Q2 Connect up circuit 2 and vary the resistance. What happens to the brightness of the lamps A and B?

Q3 Explain the difference between your observations.

Resistors
Resistors made for electronic circuits have a wide range of resistances. Electrical resistance is measured in units called **ohms** (Ω). The resistance is marked on the resistor as a colour code. The colours are in bands round the resistor.

Using the table you can work out the resistance of any resistor by using the colour codes. The first band (1) gives the first figure of the number. The second band (2) gives the second figure. The third band (3) gives the number of noughts which follow the first two figures.

There is also a fourth band. This gives the tolerance of the resistor. The value of a particular resistor can vary slightly either side of the stated value. The lower its tolerance value, the more accurate is the value of the resistor.

Tolerance: red ±2%, gold ±5%, silver ±10%. Always read the value of the resistor with the tolerance band on the right.

For the resistor shown above brown is 1, red is 2 and yellow is 4. So the resistance is 120 000 Ω or 120 kΩ.
$$1000 \, \Omega = 1 \, k\Omega$$
The tolerance is ±10%. Its value could be as low as 108 kΩ or as high as 132 kΩ.

Q4 Work out the resistance of these colour coded resistors using the table. No tolerance band is shown.

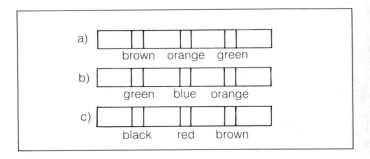

a) brown orange green
b) green blue orange
c) black red brown

Q5 Which of the resistors in Q4 has the highest resistance?

Q6 Draw the colour coded resistors which have resistances of:
a) 1000 Ω; b) 3300 Ω; c) 2000 Ω.
All should have a tolerance of 10%

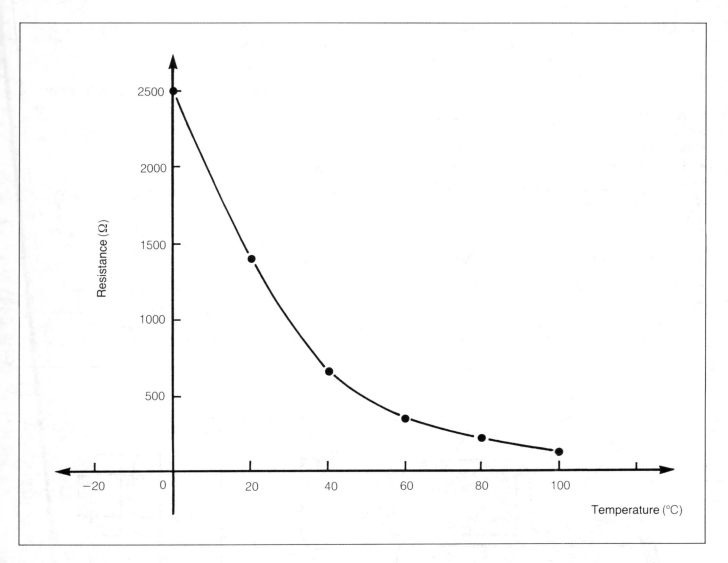

When the temperature of a thermistor changes, its resistance also changes. A thermistor is called a temperature dependent resistor. The experiment on page 7 of the students' book showed that the resistance decreases as the temperature of the thermistor increases.

The graph above shows how the resistance of a thermistor varies with different temperatures.

Q1 Does the resistance change uniformly (evenly) with temperature?

Q2 What is the resistance at:
a) 50 °C;   b) 90 °C;   c) 40 °C?

Q3 At what temperature does the thermistor have a resistance of:
a) 1000 Ω;   b) 500 Ω;   c) 300 Ω?

Q4 What is the change in resistance when the temperature changes:
a) from 0 °C to 10 °C;
b) from 90 °C to 100 °C?

Q5 Between which of the temperature ranges in Q4 is the thermistor more sensitive to temperature change?

Q6 If you kept on increasing the temperature would the resistance ever become zero? Explain your answer.

Q7 Estimate the resistance at:
a) −10 °C; b) 110 °C.
To do this you will need to plot the graph and change the scale on the vertical axis.

Extends Electronics pages 6–7

The electric motor of a lift needs a large amount of electricity (**current**) to flow through it. It would not be safe for this current to flow through the switches on the control panel in the lift. A relay can be used to switch on a current in another circuit.

In the lift there are two circuits – a control circuit and a motor circuit. A relay connects the two circuits. A small current in the control circuit can be used to switch on the large current in the motor circuit.

When an electric current passes through a coil of wire, the coil acts as a magnet. An iron rod, placed in the coil, is pushed out of the coil when the current flows. This idea is used in a car starter relay.

Current is measured in units called **ampères** (A). The starter motor of a car (shown below) needs a large current (about 100 ampères) to start turning the engine.

Q1 Why is it not safe to switch on the starter motor circuit directly?

When you turn the starter switch (or key) a small current passes through the coil.

Q2 What happens to the iron rod?

Q3 What happens when the copper plate touches the contacts?

When the car engine is running, you turn off the starter switch.

Q4 What happens to the coil?

Q5 What pushes the iron rod back to its original position?

By pressing your finger on the rubber cap on the starter motor, the iron rod can be pushed along to touch the contacts.

Q6 When would you want to do this?

Q7 Only thin wire is used in the coils. The contacts and wires to the starter motor are very thick. Explain why this is necessary.

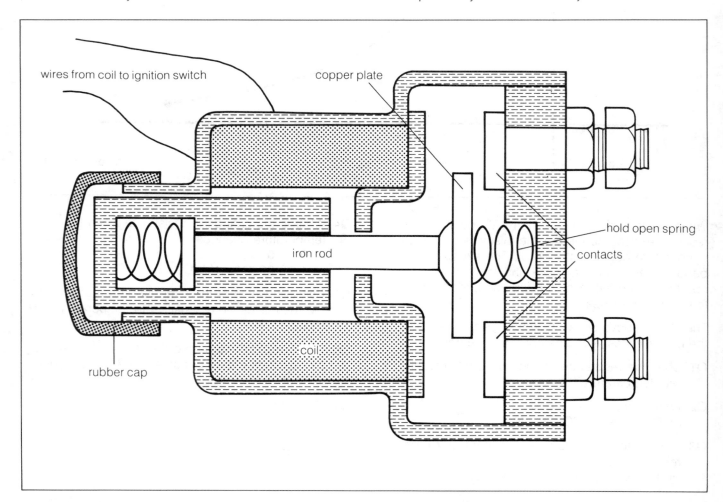

A transistor has three contacts. These are called the base, the collector and the emitter. The diagram below shows the BC108 transistor and its circuit symbol.

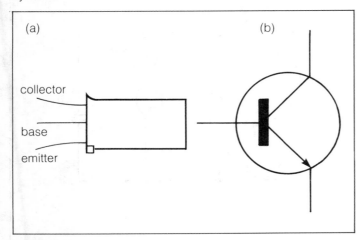

In the experiment on page 16 of the students' book, you saw that a small current in the base circuit allows a larger current to flow in the collector circuit. This can be investigated by using the circuit shown below. The amount of current flowing in a circuit can be measured with an **ammeter**. An ammeter is shown by the symbol A.

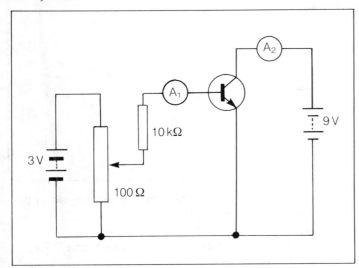

Q1 Which ammeter measures:
  a) the current in the base circuit;
  b) the current in the collector circuit?

Q2 What is the purpose of the 100 Ω variable resistor?

Q3 What is the reason for connecting the 100 Ω resistor in the base circuit?

The results of the investigation can be plotted as a graph of the collector current against the base current as is shown below. The collector current is measured in **milliampères** (mA).

$$1000\,mA = 1\,A$$

The base current is measured in microampères (μA).

$$1\,000\,000\,μA = 1\,A$$

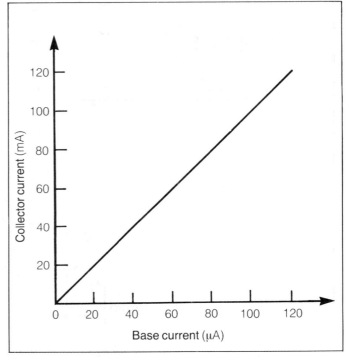

Q4 How many microampères are there in one milliampère?

Q5 How much bigger is the collector current than the base current?

Q6 If the base current changes by 20 μA, what is the change in the collector current?

The transistor can be used as an amplifier. A changing current (signal) in the base circuit will give a bigger change in the collector circuit.

$$\text{Amplification} = \frac{\text{Change in collector current}}{\text{Change in base current}}$$

Q7 What amplification does this transistor produce?

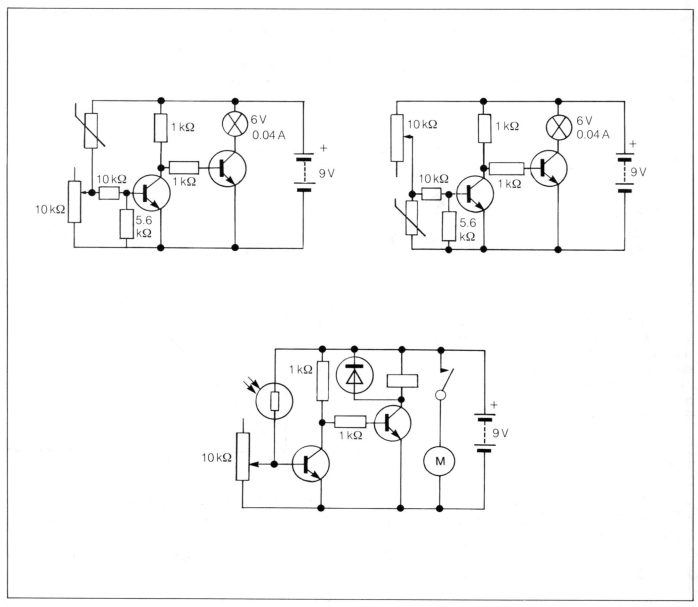

Q1 The symbol for a variable resistor is shown below. It is used in each of the circuits shown at the top of the page. What does it do in each circuit?

Q1 The symbol for a variable resistor is shown below. It is used in each of the circuits shown at the top of the page. What does it do in each circuit?

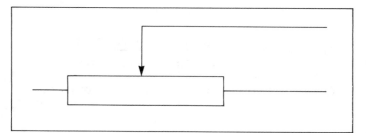

Q2 What will happen if transistors are connected the wrong way round in a circuit?

Q3 Rearrange the components that are shown in the circuit diagrams to build:
  a) a fire alarm connected to a bell;
  b) a circuit to turn off a lamp when an LDR is covered;
  c) a motor that is controlled by temperature.

Q4 Which of the six circuits (including those in Q3) would be best to:
  a) close greenhouse windows when it gets cold;
  b) operate a fan in a storage heater?

Q5 a) What problems would there be in designing a circuit to close greenhouse windows?
  b) How would you solve these problems?

Extends Electronics pages 19–22

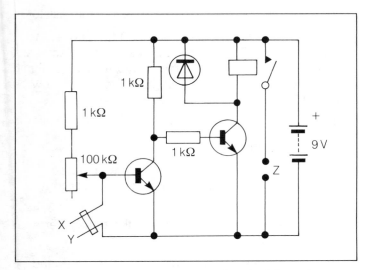

The circuit shown above was used to build a rain alarm (see page 23 of the students' book). It will also detect water in other situations. The probes can be used to give a signal when tea reaches the top of a cup. This would be useful for a blind person.

Q1 Name one other use of the water-detecting probes for a blind person.

Q2 Design a probe which could easily be used to detect when a tea cup is full. You should be able to use the probe in cups of different sizes.

The circuit can be changed to detect dryness. With this circuit there will be no signal when the probes are in water. But the alarm will sound when the probes are dry.

Q3 Draw a circuit diagram for a dryness alarm.

The circuit can be connected to probes in a water tank. When the level gets too low, an alarm sounds.

Q4 In a tank there is a valve which can be opened to let in water. The valve is powered by a motor. Draw a circuit diagram which will open the valve when the water level gets too low.

Q5 What else would you need to stop water over-flowing from the tank?

Q6 How would you use a dryness alarm in a greenhouse?

7 Light emitting diodes and phototransistors

Electronics

A light emitting diode (LED) glows when enough electricity passes through it. LEDs (shown below) can be made in different sizes. The larger ones have their own lens. This helps to concentrate the light they give out. Small LEDs are used in calculators.

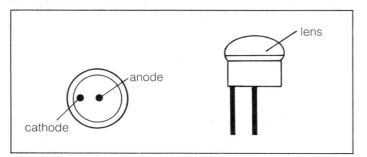

A phototransistor (shown below) also has a lens. Light shining on the lens is focused onto a sensitive junction. This changes the resistance of the transistor. This means that the collector-emitter current can be changed by shining light onto the phototransistor.

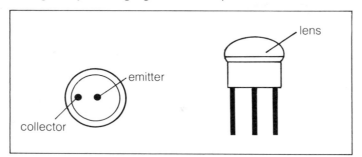

Q1 How can you tell an LED from a phototransistor?

Sound can be transmitted using an LED and a phototransistor. The sound is changed into electrical signals, which are then changed into a beam of light. The diagram at the bottom of the page shows how the light is sent and received.

Q2 Which is the transmitter?

Q3 Which is the receiver?

To send a message the transmitter needs to be connected to a microphone and the receiver to a loudspeaker.

Q4 What else is needed between the transmitter and the microphone?

Q5 What else is needed between the receiver and the loudspeaker?

Q6 What would happen if someone walked through the light beam while a message was being sent?

Q7 What would happen if the convex lenses were removed? Explain your answer.

Q8 Would this system be useful for sending messages over long distances? Explain your answer.

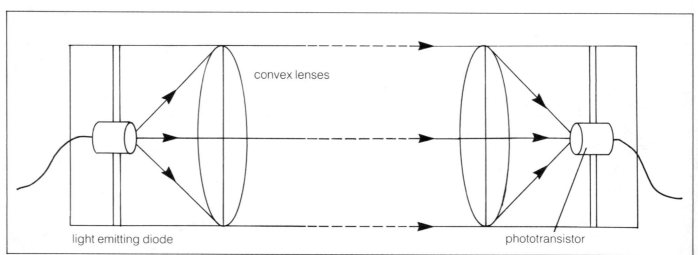

light emitting diode   convex lenses   phototransistor

Extends Electronics page 25

You have been building circuits from many electronic components. In another type of circuit, an **integrated circuit**, the whole circuit is made from one piece of material. An integrated circuit can contain hundreds of components in one small piece of silicon less than 3 mm square. This is called a **chip**.

The development of integrated circuits has meant that electronic devices, such as computers, radios and calculators, can be made much smaller. In a typical amplifier, 20 transistors, 11 resistors and a capacitor can fit on a chip no bigger than your fingernail.

The ZN414 is a chip which can be used to amplify the signals received by a radio. To improve a radio receiver, the diode is replaced by this amplifier, as shown below.

Q1 How many contacts are used on the ZN414?

Q2 What do the symbols at L_1 and L_2 represent?

Q3 The switch S changes the waveband from medium wave (MW) to long wave (LW). Which coil(s) are used for:
a) medium wave reception;
b) long wave reception?

Q4 a) What is the component VC?
b) What is its purpose in the circuit?

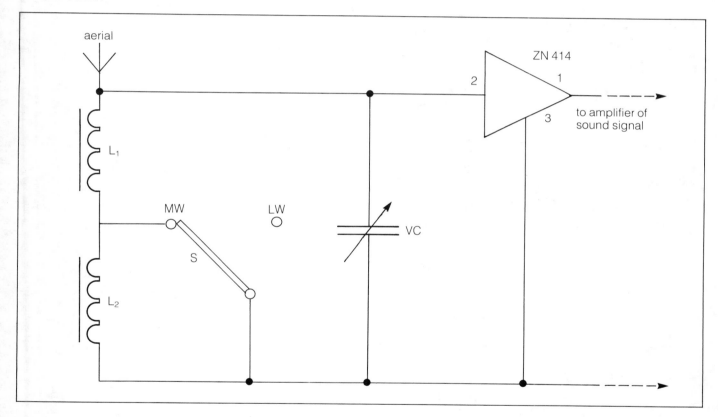

Extends Electronics pages 26–27

RESOURCES

T. Duncan, *Adventures with Electronics*, John Murray Ltd, 1978

T. Duncan, *Electronics for Today and Tomorrow*, John Murray Ltd, 1985

I. Findlay and M. Smith, *Modular Science: Electronics*, Blackie, 1979

G. E. Foxcroft, J. L. Lewis and M. K. Summers, *Electronics*, Longman, 1986

G. E. Foxcroft, J. L. Lewis and M. K. Summers, *Electronics 11–13*, Longman 1986

Schools Council, *Modular Courses in Technology: Electronics – Pupils' Book*, Oliver & Boyd, 1979

R. A. Sparkes, *Electronics*, Hutchinson and Co. Ltd, 1978